'ICE SCREAM!'

TIMMY HAS MADE ANOTHER DISGUSTING ICE CREAM FOR GRANDAD! CAN YOU HELP THEM FIGURE OUT WHAT REVOLTING INGREDIENTS ARE INSIDE IT?

V	T	D	T	D	L	C	R
Q	T	U	E	L	E	G	E
S	H	P	N	L	T	L	P
W	A	B	E	A	T	O	P
T	J	R	G	F	U	J	I
E	Y	H	D	U	C	V	K
L	S	G	N	I	E	F	C
J	P	L	I	T	N	E	L
T	U	R	N	I	P	E	B
C	A	B	B	A	G	E	L

FANTON

SOLUTION!

TICK 'EM OFF AS YOU FIND THEM!

INGREDIENTS:

TUNA ☐ LENTIL ☐ CABBAGE ☐ TURNIP ☐ KIPPER ☐
LETTUCE ☐ SARDINE ☐ CELERY ☐

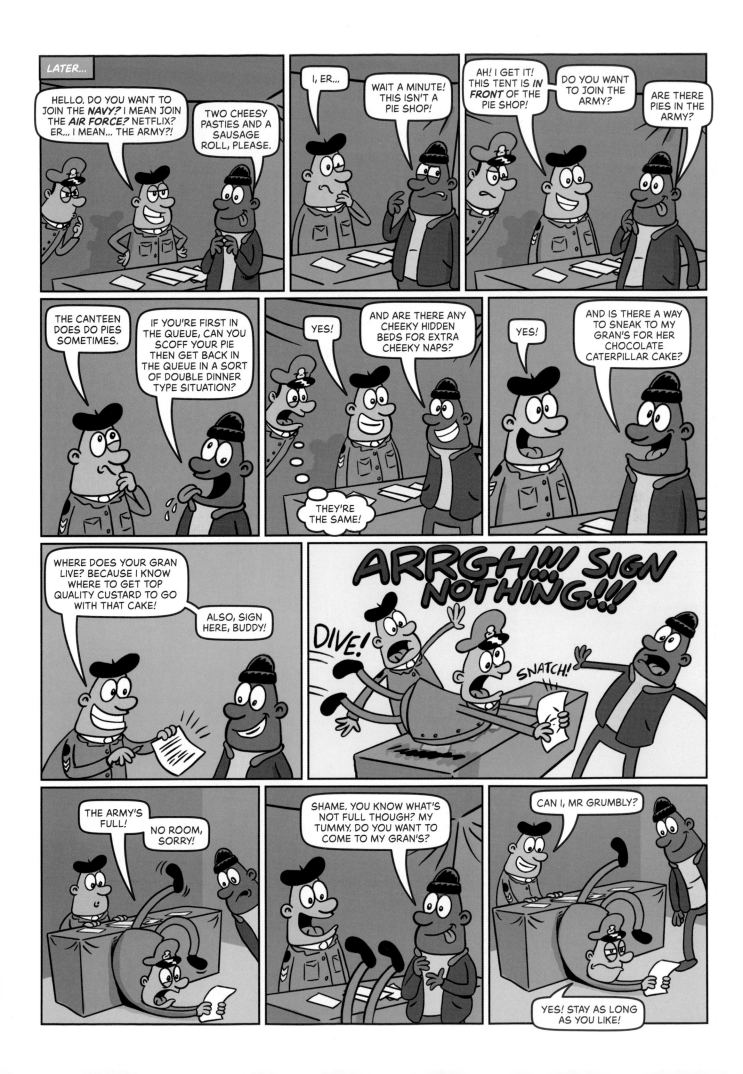

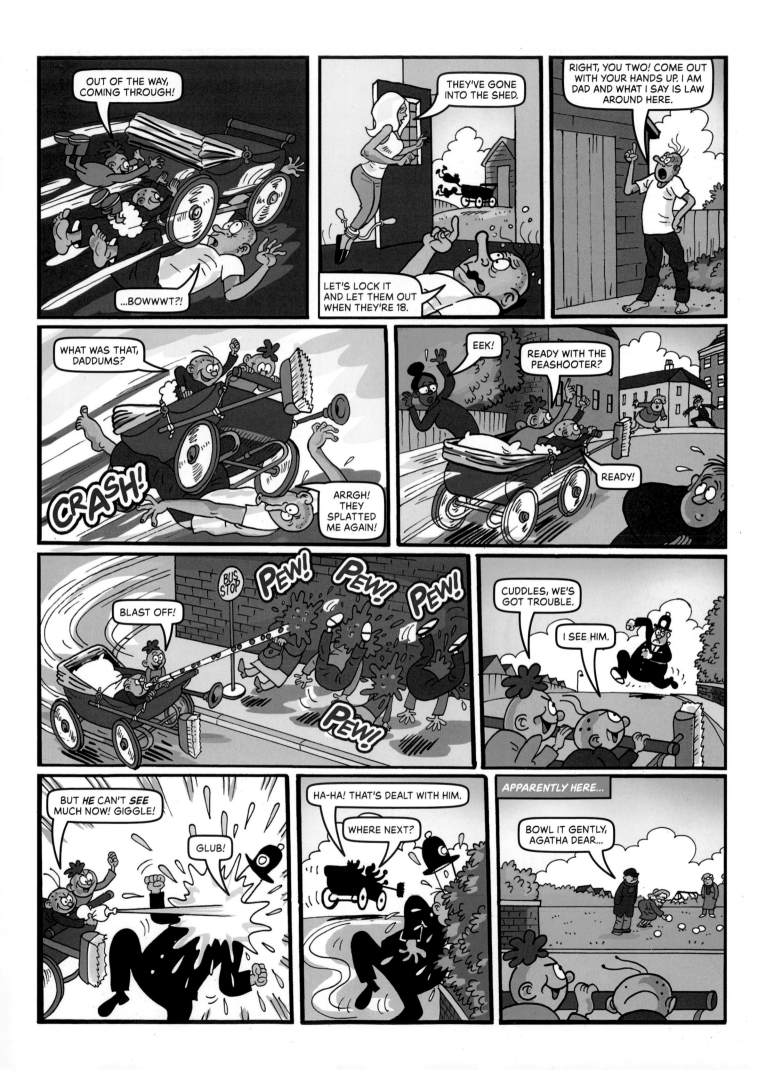

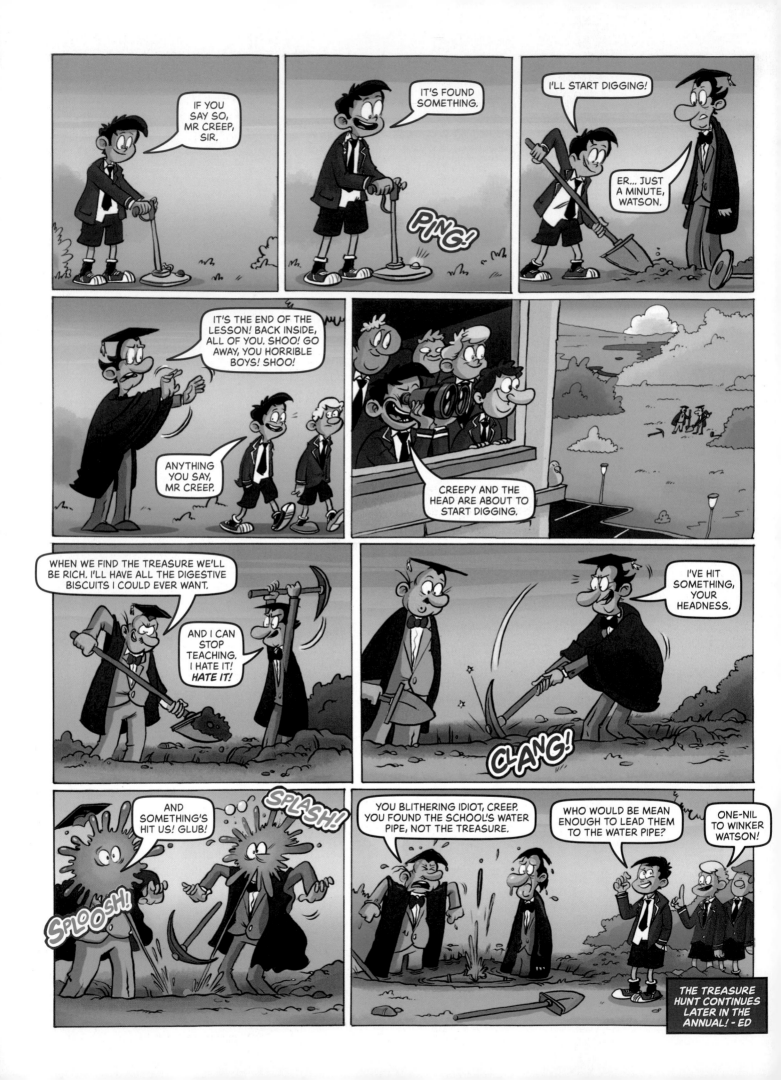

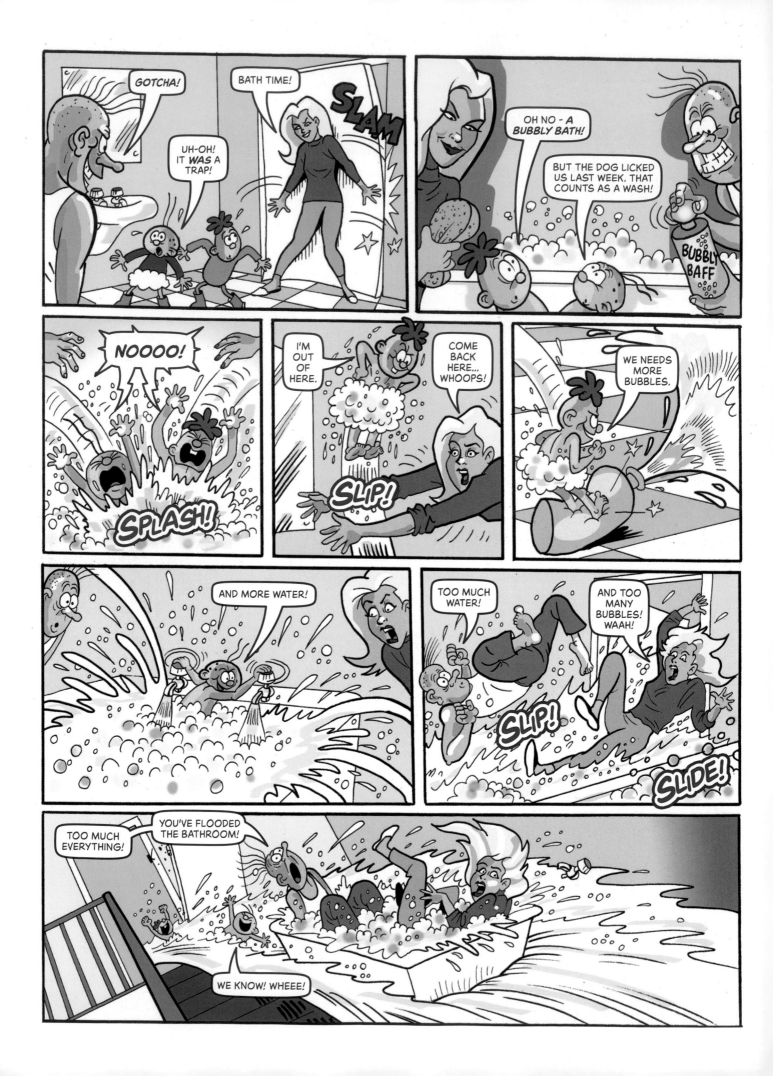

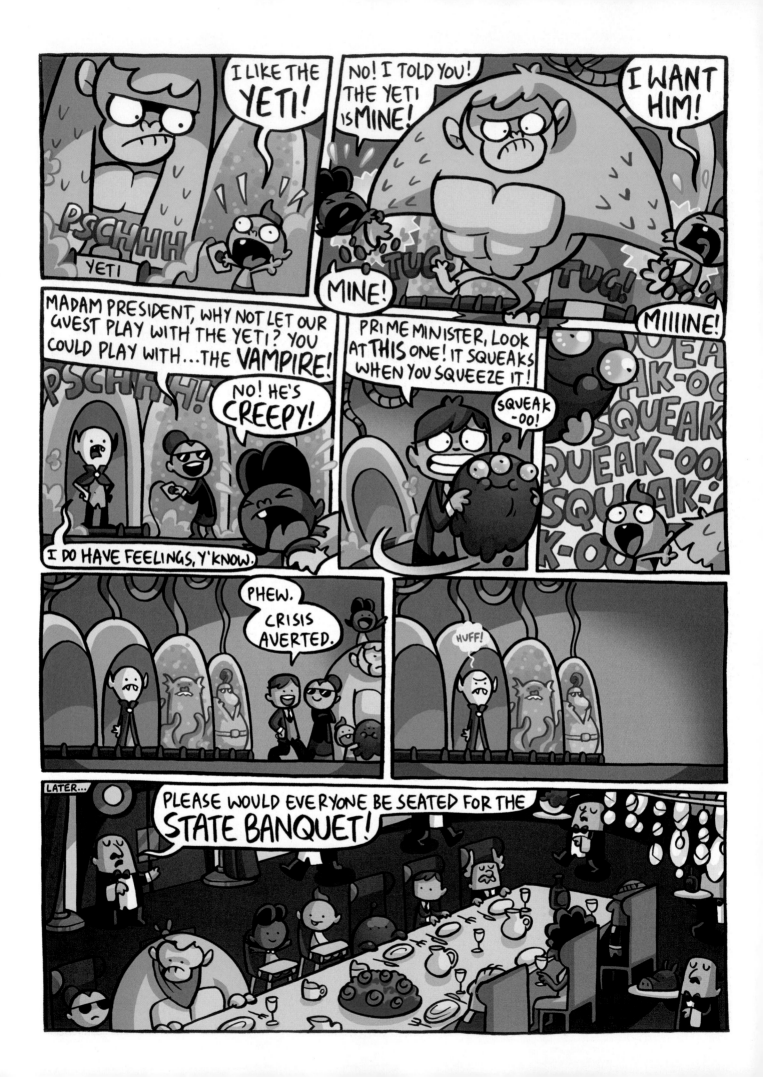

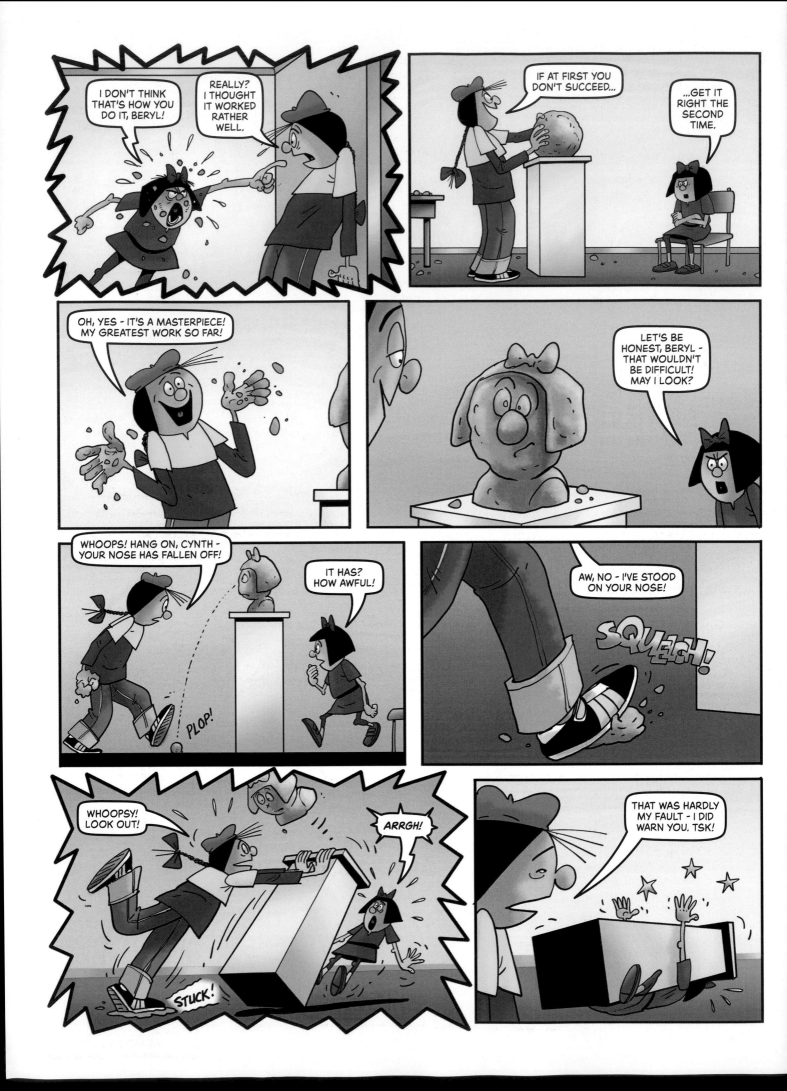

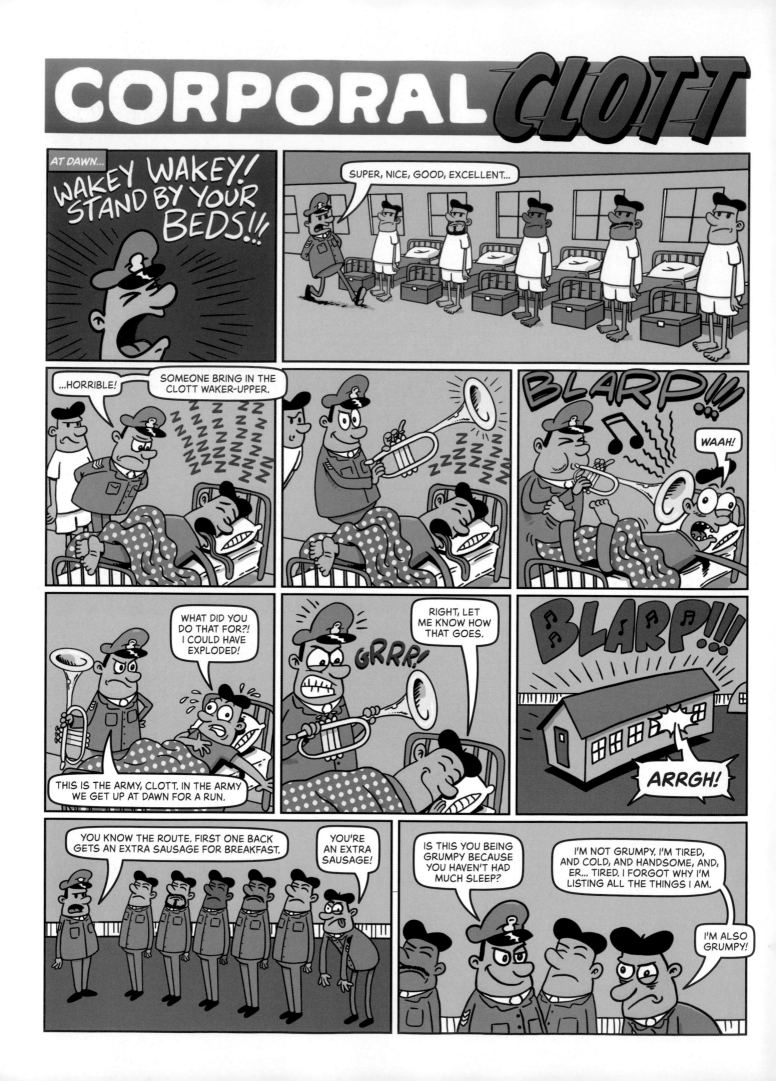

DON'T CRY OVER SPILT... PAINT!

Cuddles and Dimples pranked their parents with this awesome fake paint spill! Here's how to do it!

WHAT YOU'LL NEED:

- [ ] Craft paint
- [ ] PVA glue
- [ ] Greaseproof paper

1

Pick the colour of paint you want for your spill. Mix it together with the same amount of glue until it gets sticky.

2

Pour it onto greaseproof paper and leave it to dry overnight. Keep it hidden so your parents don't rumble your prank.

3 Once dry, leave it on the floor somewhere your parents will see and put a paintbrush beside it. You can also use this recipe to make fake coffee, milk or other spills!

WARNING: DO NOT PLACE ON CARPET!

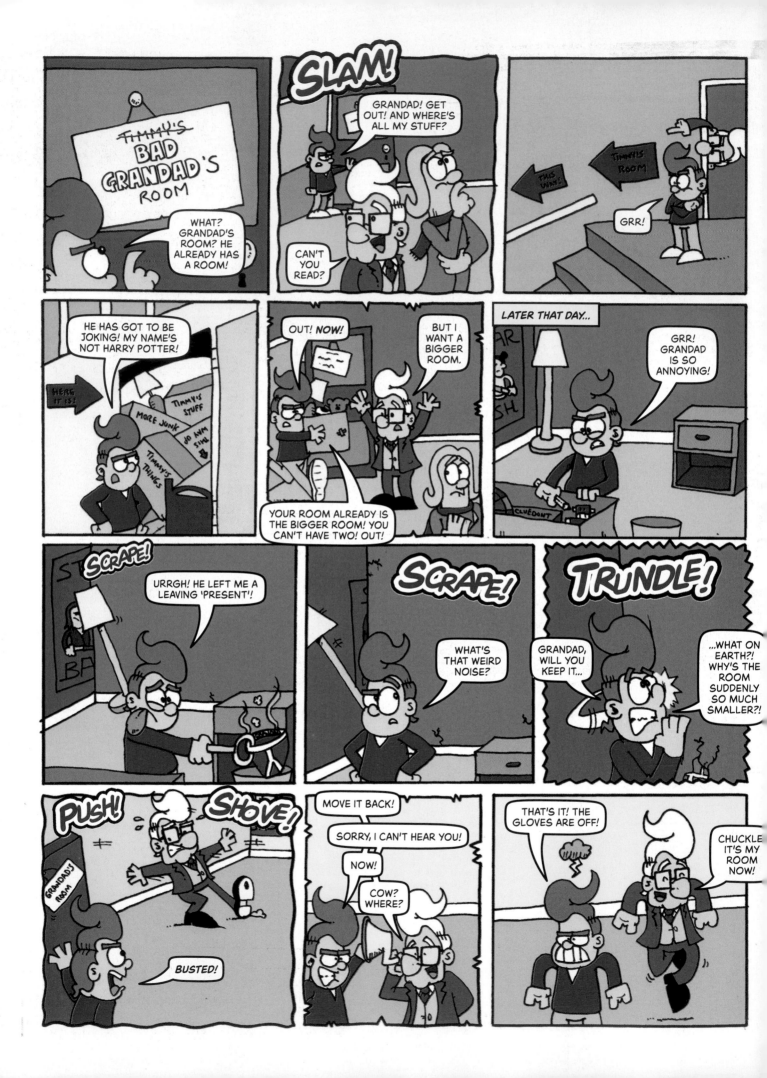

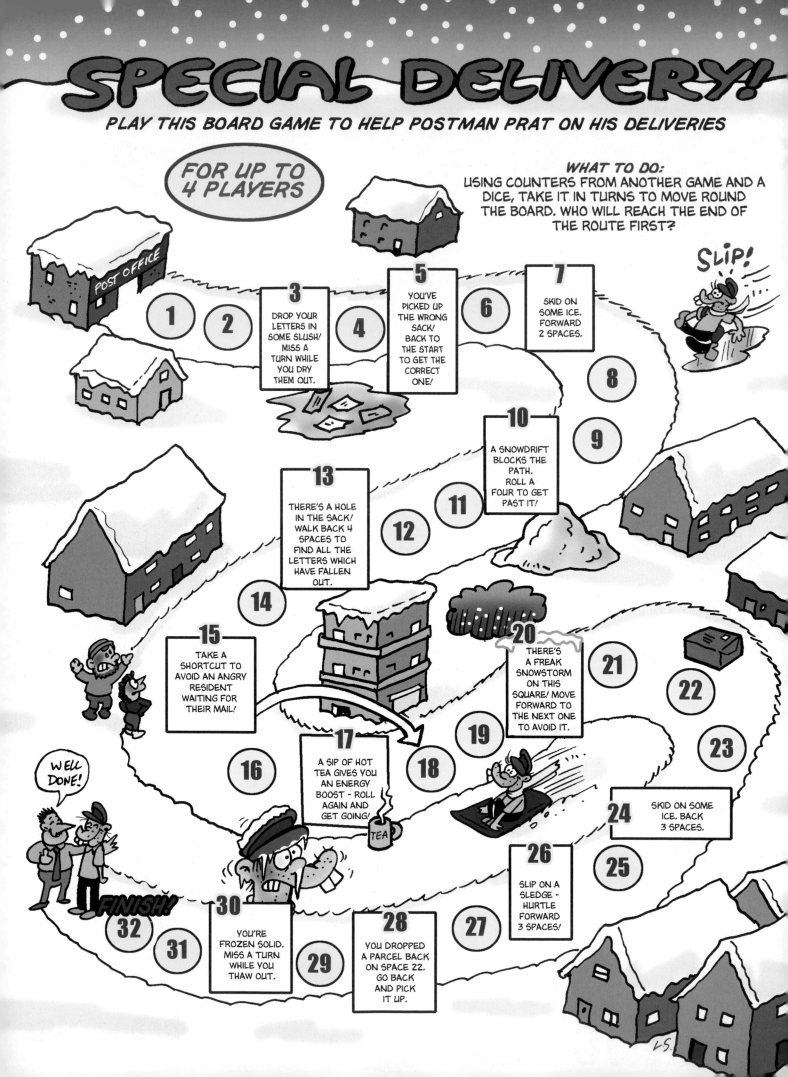